THE CAP

PEARSON

Glenview, Illinois • Boston, Massachusetts • Chandler, Arizona
Shoreview, Minnesota • Upper Saddle River, New Jersey

Jack!

My cap is blue.

I like my cap.

I like Jack!

We like the cap!

We like Jack!

ISBN-13: 978-0-328-38912-4
ISBN-10:   0-328-38912-9

3 4 5 6 7 8 9 10 V054 17 16 15 14 13 12 11 10

Get Set, Roll!

Reader 10

Jon Scieszka's
Trucktown
on Reading Street

Story by
Dennis Fertig

Tune-up by
Jacqui Briggs

Illustrations by
Luis Contreras
Michael Spooner

Created by Jon Scieszka.
Characters and environments
developed by

design garage

David Shannon, Loren Long, and David Gord⟨⟩
Illustration crew: Executive Producer: Keytoon⟨⟩
⟨⟩ in association with Animagic S.L.
Creative Supervisor: Sergio Pablos.
Drawings by: Ron Pa⟨⟩
Color by: Isabel ⟨⟩zba.
Color Assistant: Gab⟨⟩
Art Director: Avi ⟨⟩

PEARSON

ISBN-13: 978-0-328-38912-4
ISBN-10: 0-328-38912-9

EAN

9 780328 389124

90000>

TRUCKTOWN and JON SCIESZKA'S TRU⟨⟩
and design are trademarks of JRS Worldw⟨⟩, LLC

T2-AGS-863